43

THE BOARD OF EDUCATION FOR THE
TOWNSHIP OF NORTH YORK

SCHOOL: .... LAMBERTON ....

DATE: .... APR - - 1967 ....

PRICE: ....

NUMBER: .... 2176 ....

TALES THE TOTEMS TELL

Tales the Totems Tell

by

HUGH WEATHERBY

Illustrations by the Author

TORONTO
THE MACMILLAN COMPANY
OF CANADA LIMITED
1962

**TO
CRETE**

CONTENTS

	PAGE
THE FIRST TOTEM POLE	1
THE RAVEN AND THE INDIANS	10
HOW THE FROG PEOPLE GOT THEIR TOTEM	18
HOW THE WHALE KEPT HIS PROMISE	29
THE TONGUE-LICKED PEOPLE	40
THE LEGEND OF THE THUNDERBIRD	51
THE STORY OF THE GRATEFUL WOLF	60
KAIGYET, THE STRONG MAN, or THE CROSS-EYED INDIAN PEOPLE	69
THE MYSTERY OF THE FORBIDDEN PLATEAU	80
THE MOUNTAIN GOAT OF GURHSAN	90

ILLUSTRATIONS

FACING PAGE

Before Ram's startled eyes a figure slowly rose from the middle of the spring 2

The stone figure had moved! Slowly, but surely, it was sliding downhill 6

Long ago, before the ravens even thought of becoming famous, the croaking black birds used to follow the fishing fleet and beg for food 10

With a single stab of his beak he snatched the silvery disc from its place in the sky 14

For many days the raft drifted, always washed by the down-pouring rain 20

One-whom-the-frogs-like and Bear Killer set to work carving their totem pole 26

The fishing was good and soon the tribesmen returned with their canoes loaded down with salmon, cod and halibut, which they dumped in the whale's mouth 30

Hardly had the people raised their hands to the skies than the rain came pouring down, harder even than before 36

Naturally, too, he was joined by other renegades, until he had a formidable little army at his disposal 44

Naeqt fell, shot through the breast and mortally wounded 48

He spent his time watching the carvers at work and dreaming of the day when he, too, would be a great carver 52

Like a shot the big bird dropped on the fleeing monster 56

Finally they looked in the wolf's throat, and there, sure enough, was a firmly lodged fish bone 60

FACING
PAGE

In the middle of the clearing lay five shapes, which the men knew, even before they got close, were the bodies of caribou 64

Gyaedem gasped, for on the palm of the giant's hand was the figure of a heart! 70

It was the alert Gyaedem, Kaigyet's foster-father, who first discovered the mistake 76

He was a tower of strength and from him the whole tribe drew courage and confidence 82

The Comoxes waited tensely, every eye on Little Bear. The Albernis continued their noisy advance 86

As Gurhsan and the goat were picking their way along the trail a scream rent the air from some distance to the right 92

Travellers, both Indian and white, pause on their way through the village to admire the fine totem poles 96

TALES THE TOTEMS TELL

The First Totem Pole

WHEN Ramlaryaelk was very young, perhaps three or four years old, a medicine man told his mother that the boy would one day do something to make him remembered forever by the Indians.

As Ram—we will call Ramlaryaelk Ram for short—walked along the banks of the Footprints-in-the-shallow-water River near the upper reaches of the Skeena, he thought of the old prophecy, and how, even though he was nearly thirty, no chance had yet come for him to make himself famous. True, with his two brothers, he had engaged in many battles and proved his mettle, but all young Indian men fought like heroes in the never-ending wars. Perhaps, he thought, chuckling to himself, he would live to such a ripe old age that the tribal singers would make up songs about his doings and sing them to future generations.

His day-dreams were interrupted by a call from a nearby camp. "Ram," cried a stern voice, "take a basket and get some water from the Spring-that-always-boils."

Ram picked up a waterproof basket—the Indians wove baskets so fine they easily held water—and ran to do as he was bidden, for, as he and his brothers were only adopted sons of the Larsail, having once belonged to the Wild Rice tribe, they

1

were made to do some of the unpleasant chores to show they were not quite as good as the Larsail men.

Ram found his two brothers sitting by the Spring-that-always-boils. It was late in the fall and quite cold, but the air around the spring was warm and comfortable. He greeted his brothers and they nodded in return, as was the custom, and then he stooped to fill the cedar-root basket with hot water. That move was never finished.

Before Ram's startled eyes a figure slowly rose from the middle of the spring. It seemed to be the statue of a man in a sitting position, with his hands pressed against his side. Seven young ravens rested on top of its head, which, like the rest of its body, was as bare of clothing as a new-born baby.

The three young men froze and stared, open-mouthed. Their feelings ran from fear to wonder and back to fear again. Ram was the first to recover his wits and he quickly turned towards the village and called for help, to bring the rest of the tribe to the scene so that there might be witnesses outside his own immediate family, for he realized, even in that short time, that the tale, unless others saw the strange sight, would be greeted with jeers and laughter.

All the villagers within earshot came pelting down to the spring. As they arrived they, like Ram and his brothers, froze rigid for a second, their eyes bulging out, and then took up the chorus of "Ohs" and "Ahs" and gaped in amazement. The Indians cackled among themselves like a flock of geese disturbed by some prowler in the night. Surely nothing like this had ever before been seen by mortal man!

When the excitement died down a little, Ram sent a pair of his friends to bring tools while the rest of the tribe prepared to take the statue from the spring to firmer ground. "See," he said happily, "this is the beginning of the fortune the witch

Before Ram's startled eyes a figure slowly rose from the middle of the spring.

doctor told for me. From now on, with this at the door of our lodge, none will deny my brothers and me equal rights with the Larsail men."

"That is so," nodded one of the old men, "with such a totem before your door, who would dare say you should not have equal rights?"

The task of moving the figure to Ram's home proved more than any of them expected, and finally it was decided that the spring would have to be drained.

The work of digging drains took several hours, but at last the statue rested on dry, or at least fairly dry, land. The Indians hitched on their cedar ropes and made ready to pull the stone figure up the hill. Once again they found the figure too heavy, and, tug as they might, it moved not an inch.

After several attempts, and much grunting by the fatter Indians, Ram raised his hand in a signal to stop. "We must have help," he said. "We will call in the Wolf, Fireweed and Larhaun tribes; we have helped them in the past and they will gladly help us now."

With the aid of the newcomers the figure was moved quickly up the hill and placed before Ram's door.

Ram looked it over with pleasure and satisfaction; pleasure because there was nothing else like it in the country, and satisfaction because it meant equal rights for his brothers and himself with the Larsail men. Ram's breast almost burst with pride. Surely, he thought, this is the time to give a huge feast and show my find to the neighbouring tribes, and at the same time repay my own people for their help in getting the figure up here.

The news of the feast spread far and wide, as such news always does among the Indians, for they love a big feast or potlatch, and, two days before the date set, members of some

of the more distant tribes began drifting in. As more and more
guests came Ram grew prouder and prouder; his fame would
grow as the stories of the statue and feast were told and retold
by his guests, till everyone on the river would know of
Ramlaryaelk and the stone image he owned.

Ram stood before his lodge on the eve of the big feast and
thought of the future with pleasure. From time to time he
glanced fondly at the statue. Suddenly he straightened up,
blinked his eyes, spat out the twig he was chewing, and
gasped. The stone figure had moved! Slowly and surely it
was sliding downhill! Even as Ram opened his mouth to cry
for help, the statue gave another, harder lurch, picked up
speed and slid with a grinding of stones and mad scattering
of mud, past a few startled, staring Indian people, down the
steep slope, and splashed into the lake. There was nothing
left to mark its passing but a deep muddy ditch.

For a few seconds the poor man was too stunned to move,
then he rushed to the water's edge, dropped to his knees, and
peered hopefully into the green depths. There was nothing to
be seen. The stone figure had already sunk from sight.

Ram tottered back to his lodge. He stumbled inside and
sank down on a pile of furs, unable to believe his bad luck.
He sat on his haunches and rocked back and forth, muttering
to himself. "I am doomed! I am doomed! And just when I
had a chance to become an equal member of the tribe. Surely
the spirits are against me."

His mother heard his moans and looked in. After asking
the cause of his grief, she sat down beside him. "Poor, poor
Ram," she murmured, "to have this happen just when you
were so near to success."

"If I could only find another statue, mother, to put in the
place of the one I lost," he sobbed, "then it might not be so

The stone figure had moved! Slowly, but surely, it was sliding downhill!

bad; but to have no statue to show, that is sad beyond words. We will never live down the shame, it will follow us forever."

"Could you not carve one from wood?" the old woman asked.

Ram sat up with a jerk. That was the answer. A wooden statue carved as nearly like the stone one as he could remember. He jumped to his feet, patted his mother lovingly, and ran to ask the help of his brothers and his fellow-tribesmen. He knew they would all help, for, if no statue appeared at the feast, the honour of the whole tribe would be at stake.

The next day, the day of the big feast, Ram took his place beside the door of his hut, with his hand resting lightly on the head of the newly carved, grey-painted, wooden figure. As he greeted his guests, one and all remarked about the statue and to each he told the story of how he came by it. The last guest finally passed and not a soul, except the members of his own tribe, dreamed that the figure they admired was not the image dragged from the hot-water spring.

Ram watched the merry-makers through half-shut eyes. This was indeed his big day, for now he was a full-fledged member of the tribe. Surely this was the day the medicine man spoke about, the one that would make him known to history.

Ram was right, too. That was his big day, but, not, as he thought, because he gave a potlatch and displayed a statue to his friends, but because from that day on the Indians of the northern Pacific coast carved figures of wood. Ramlaryaelk had, without meaning to, invented the totem pole.

The Raven and the Indians

OF all the figures found on poles carved around Massett, near the northern end of the Queen Charlotte Islands, the raven is by far the most common. Clutched tightly in its beak, the bird holds a disc, something like a saucer, which is supposed to be the moon. The story of how the raven came to be so important to the Massett Indians goes back many, many years; so many, in fact, that only the oldest men can remember hearing the story from people living at that time.

Long ago, before the ravens even thought of becoming famous, one of the croaking black birds used to follow the fishing fleet and beg for food. Kindly Indians tossed bits of fish to him, now and again. But, year by year, this raven got lazier and lazier, and finally, instead of hunting for himself, he spent all his time flapping around the fishing boats. When the men tired of feeding him he would watch his chance and, as soon as they were all busy with their lines, he would swoop down and steal the finest fish from their catch. This so angered the Indians that they vowed, come rain or shine, they would feed the greedy bird no more.

When they told the raven this he flew into a terrible rage and swooped about the boats squawking horrible threats at men who had been his friends. At last the Indians tired of

Long ago, before the ravens even thought of becoming famous,
the croaking black birds used to follow the fishing fleet and beg
for food.

his noisy bad temper and drove him away with stones. This angered the bird still more. He flew away, but, just before he passed from sight, he screamed back over his shoulder, "When the Oolichans start to run, I'll have my revenge. Just you wait!"

The Indians were afraid in spite of themselves, for the Oolichans—small, oily fish about the size of smelt—provided them with most of their oil, both for cooking and lighting. A bad Oolichan year was about the worst bad luck that could befall the tribe. But, they asked themselves, what in the world could a silly raven do? What, indeed! After thinking it over, it seemed foolish to worry, so they shrugged their shoulders and went back to their fishing.

By the time the Oolichan run started, most of the Indians had forgotten all about the raven and his threats. So on the first night of fishing—Oolichans are fished by the light of the moon—they were startled and surprised to hear the hoarse voice of the raven in the darkness overhead. "Wait till the moon comes out," he cried, and there seemed to be a note of triumph in his tone. "Just you wait!"

The poor fishermen were struck dumb with fear. It was most unusual for a raven to be out after dark. Perhaps, after all, he could do something to spoil the Oolichan catch. Strange tales were told of the Evil One taking the shape of animals, maybe he could also take the shape of a bird—the raven, for instance.

The moon came up slowly, tracing a silvery path across the water. The Indians huddled in the bottoms of their canoes and shivered with fear. Nothing happened. An hour passed, and still nothing happened. The moon continued her rise into the sky, and, as it grew lighter, the bolder fishermen recovered a little from their fear and peered this way and that into the night. The raven was nowhere to be seen.

"Tush," laughed the chief at last, "how silly to let a foolish bird upset us. Come, let's get on with our Oolichan fishing."

Just as the nets were out, the raven came flapping his way over the inlet. At first the Indians were startled, then as they saw it was just an ordinary raven, the same one they had pelted with stones a few days before, the last bit of fear left them. The bird seemed to sense this for he swooped down, shouting as loudly as he could, "I am going to steal the moon, steal the moon, steal the moon. Ha, Ha, Haaaaaaaaaa . . . Then see how you like it. And see, too, how many Oolichans you catch."

The Indians roared with laughter and shouted rude remarks at their would-be tormentor. Imagine, a raven stealing the moon! Of all the silly things!

The raven screamed with rage at their laughter and, flapping his wings wildly, flew straight at the moon. With a single stab of his beak he snatched the silvery disc from its place in the sky, then he flew over the heads of the Indians, so that all might see how he made good his threats. After making three circles above the terrified tribesmen, who were again crouched and shaking in the bottoms of their canoes, he started winging his way out to sea, laughing all the while as loudly as he could without dropping the moon.

The chief cried out in fear, and raised his arms toward the bird. "Mercy, mercy," he cried, "leave us the moon. We knew not what we said. You may have all the fish you can eat. We will put you on our totem poles. Anything, only give us back the moon."

The rest of the Indians added their pleas to the chief's.

The raven paused. He was a kindly bird by nature, in spite of all his noise. Besides, perhaps he had been getting

With a single stab of his beak he snatched the silvery disc from its place in the sky.

lazy . . . and the Indians had been his good friends in the past. "Wellllllllll," he said, "if you give me fish when I ask, and put me on your totems, I'll replace the moon."

The Indians shouted their promises and the raven flew up and put the moon back in the sky.

To this very day the Indians who live near Massett, on the Queen Charlotte Islands, always toss a piece of fish to any raven who asks for it, and all the children of the Indians who made the promise keep the raven on their totems. The ravens, on their part, have never since touched the moon.

How the Frog People Got Their Totem

THE people of the village crouched in the doorways of their bark huts and watched the down-pouring rain and ever-rising Skeena River with troubled anxious eyes, for this was the fiftieth day of the deluge. Never in the memory of the tribe had it rained so long or so much, nor had the river ever risen to its present height. The people shook with fear as they huddled down and watched.

The old chief of Skeena village (we will call the village "Skeena" because it was located at the mouth of the Skeena River, and because the old story-tellers did not pass on the name they used for it) spoke softly to his people, trying to comfort them, though he well knew the danger that was to come.

"See," he said, "does it not seem lighter, as though the sun were about to shine? Surely tomorrow will bring sunshine to dry away the tears of the angry spirits."

"Aih, aih, aih," moaned the tribesmen, "aih, aih, aih. The sun is lost forever. We shall all die. The spirits have been offended."

The brave chieftain turned to his wife, "It is no use, they already know the truth. It is just as our daughter, One-whom-

18

the-frogs-like, saw in her dream. The water will destroy us all."

Hearing her name, One-whom-the-frogs-like raised her head and lifted her eyes from the hide she had been stitching. Her two children, a little boy of four and a baby girl, feeling their mother move, also stirred and raised their eyes to look at their grandparents.

"There is a way out," said the young woman, "just as I told you in my dream. First, get the tribe together and have them build rafts, and store them well with plenty of food and fur robes. We will have to drift for days, maybe weeks, before the flood lessens enough for us to land again."

The old man nodded. It was the only suggestion that had been offered, and at least the work of getting ready would keep the people busy and take their minds off the raging waters.

The building of the rafts went forward rapidly, as work done by hands driven by fear usually does. The logs were hauled in and lashed together. Rude bark shelters were built on them. Baskets full of food were tied firmly to the logs, and warm furs were piled high inside the shelters. Hurry, hurry, hurry, was the watchword. Speed, lest the waters overtake us before the work is completed.

For seven days and seven nights the labour was pushed forward, with most of the men staying on the job until they dropped in their tracks. They slept where they fell, and when they had rested they rose and again took up their tasks.

On the seventh night, the rain increased to a solid mass of falling water. Streams formed in the village and quickly grew to the size of raging rivers. Huts collapsed under the weight of the downpour; goods and supplies were whipped away in the flood.

Panic seized the Indians. Braves who ordinarily would have died fighting to save their children and wives, rushed about in aimless terror, trampling pitilessly on those who got in their way. They plunged through the raging waters to where the rafts were anchored, and the stronger scrambled aboard, pushing the weaker back into the water, and beating off with paddles those who tried to catch the rafts as they passed. The women and children, naturally, had small chance in this scramble for life. They were quickly beaten down and left to the mercy of the torrent.

The old chieftain waded out into the stream to stop his maddened warriors, but they were past all reason and struck him down, and held him beneath the water until he stopped struggling. His wife screamed with horror and fought her way to her husband's side. Together they were swept away by the swollen stream.

One-whom-the-frogs-like crouched in the shelter of a fallen hut, with her children held close to her body and protected by the folds of her ample robe. She watched the panic with calm eyes. This was as her dream had pictured, although she had not told her father about the bad conduct of his braves; this was as she had expected. Neither, then, was it any surprise to her to see a raft come drifting towards her, after the other members of the tribe had disappeared. Pushing the raft were hundreds of frogs, whom she greeted as old friends, and who answered her with hoarse croaks. She lifted her little son and baby daughter onto the raft and then climbed up beside them. The frogs, slowly and gently, guided the rough craft and its burden out into the stream.

For many days the raft drifted, always washed by the drenching downpour of rain. During the first days they had been able to see mountain peaks from time to time, but those

For many days the raft drifted, always washed by the down-pouring rain.

finally dropped from sight, leaving only the rolling, tossing, apparently limitless, expanse of water.

And always the rain beat down endlessly.

The heavy rain was a blessing in a way because it kept the water fresh on the surface of the sea for a depth of several feet, and so enabled the frogs to continue with the raft, even after the river's mouth was far behind. Had the water been salt the frogs would have died in a very short time.

As it was, they stayed at their posts and kept the raft always pointed into the wind, and at the same time gently nosing it in a direction known only to themselves. From time to time One-whom-the-frogs-like spoke to her friends, asking them where they were taking her. Each time they replied that they did not know, but were guided by an inner urge to swim in a certain direction, which they were sure would lead them to safety.

One day the oldest frog, who was the leader, raised his voice and croaked to his companions, "We must hurry, the water is getting salt again, which means the rains are nearly over. We cannot stand salt water for very long. Hurry, my friends, hurry!"

It had been the habit of the frogs, during the early part of the voyage, to rest for the night, leaving just enough of their number on duty to keep the raft headed in the right direction; but now that changed and the frogs took regular shifts, working as hard as they could. Their leader urged them on, continually crying for more and more speed.

Early one morning, when the rains had almost stopped and the water had become so salt the frogs could hardly stand it, a dim cloud appeared on the horizon. Larger and larger it loomed until, by mid-morning, the refugees were able to tell that it was land. To add to their joy a wet trickle of sunlight glinted off some of the higher peaks. They were safe at last.

The frogs swam directly into the mouth of a river, just as though they had been there a thousand times before. One-whom-the-frogs-like leapt ashore and tied the raft to an overhanging spruce.

Once the humans were safe on shore the frogs plunged into the fresh water to rid themselves of salt and to wash away the weariness resulting from the last few days of overwork. The young mother, with her two children, watched the frogs frolicking in the fresh water, from time to time smiling at their romping, and thinking how good and loyal they had been to her, and how fine it was to know that they, too, were safe.

At last, tired of their sport, the frogs came ashore and took up sitting positions in an irregular semicircle around the three people.

"How can I ever thank you?" asked One-whom-the-frogs-like, looking around at her friends.

The oldest and wisest frog rumbled deep in his throat and then spoke, "You need not thank us. We did what we did because we love you very much, and also, because you are a woman of fate. Your name and fame will live long after the memory of all the rest of your people is dead. Those that are remembered at all will be remembered as someone connected with you."

The woman was puzzled, "What makes you say that?"

The old frog shook his head, "I do not know for sure," he said, "but that is what the inner voice tells me, the same voice that guided us here."

One-whom-the-frogs-like insisted on thanking the frogs, in spite of what their leader said. They beamed and blinked under her praises and promised to stay always with her and her children, and help them whenever possible.

The strange companions spent the next few days exploring the island, for they had landed on one of the Queen Charlotte Islands. One day they found an Indian camp, which seemed to be deserted. They looked around for some sign of a live human being, but found none, and they were on the verge of leaving when they heard a groan coming from under a hut that had fallen down. They rushed over and pulled aside some loose bark. There, huddled under a pile of wet hides, lay a young man. His pale face and weak breathing told them he was nearly dead, and, in addition to suffering from water and cold, he was badly wounded.

Gently the woman and her frog friends made the young man, who remained unconscious, more comfortable. They arranged his bed, replaced the wet furs with dry ones of their own, and One-whom-the-frogs-like made a broth from some supplies she had brought with her on the raft.

When the hot food touched the young man's lips, he slowly opened his eyes. He looked at One-whom-the-frogs-like with open admiration, and she returned his look. They fell in love instantly.

The story of Bear Killer, which was the young man's name, and the fair One-whom-the-frogs-like is a love story. They were married in tribal fashion as soon as the young man was well enough, and the frogs danced their delight at the wedding, for they had already become quite fond of the young man.

After several weeks a few more members of the young man's tribe returned. Some had escaped to the peaks, while others had drifted during the flood.

When the village settled down to its usual activity it became the desire of the people to do something which would make them remember their escape. After much talk it was decided that each family would carve a totem pole picturing their own adventures during the flood.

One-whom-the-frogs-like and Bear Killer set to work on their pole. The young woman wanted to make her husband's totem the top one, or foremost (Bear Killer belonged to the Bear people) but he would not hear of it. After all, he pointed out, they would both be dead if it had not been for the frogs, so, in all justice, they should place the frogs in first place, and let the frog be their family totem for ever more.

That is why the descendants of One-whom-the-frogs-like and Bear Killer always carve the frogs in the place of honour on their totem poles.

True to the old frog's prophecy the lovely One-whom-the-frogs-like, as Frog Woman, remains fresh in the memory of the Indian people, while almost everyone else who lived at the same time has been forgotten.

One-whom-the-frogs-like and Bear Killer set to work carving their totem pole.

How the Whale Kept His Promise

A LONG British Columbia's northern coast and coastal islands rain falls nearly every day, 300 inches a year— 25 feet of solid rain water.

The Indians who live there do not seem to mind the rain at all, in fact they enjoy it. When they hear a white man grumble about the wet, they smile and nod, for they know that it did not always rain so much. As a matter of fact, they know it rained very little when the land was young, and, as a result, forest fires burned the beautiful timber stands and destroyed the Indian villages. According to the tales of the local story-tellers it would still be a dry parched land but for a stranded whale and a kindly tribe of Indians.

One day, so the legend goes, a young whale swam into a shallow inlet to bask in the sun and warm himself on the shoals. The water was so pleasant that he was asleep before he knew it. All afternoon he slept, to awaken when the sun was sinking behind the western mountains. He yawned, blinked sleepily, stretched and started to swim slowly towards the open sea. Naturally enough, he went straight to the passage he had come in by, but to his surprise the tide had gone out while he slept and instead of water, a long sandbar met his anxious eyes. The poor whale had a moment of panic.

He swished around and tried another likely-looking spot, only to find that there, too, the water level had fallen, leaving a barrier of sand which he could not cross. All night long he searched in vain. There was no way out. He was trapped!

For a week he swam aimlessly about in his watery prison, watching the tide come in and go out; seeing the water rise, inch by inch, and then go back before it got high enough to allow him to escape. To make matters worse, hunger became a problem after the first day. True, there were a few fish, stranded like himself in the lagoon, but they would be only a mouthful to a hungry whale. They came so far from being a meal that he didn't even bother to pursue them.

Day by day his plight became more and more desperate, until at last, sure his fate was sealed and there could be no escape before the next big tides, which would be too late, he lay down to die.

How long he had been lying there he did not know, when he heard whispering voices close to his ear. At first he thought he must be dreaming or dead, but as he listened the voices became clearer and clearer. Cautiously he opened his eyes. There, scarcely a dozen feet away, were several Indians in their dugout canoes. At the sight of his eyes opening, the terrified natives dug their paddles into the water and sent their light craft scooting.

"Hello!" called the whale in a weak voice. "Do not be afraid. I will not hurt you. In fact, I'm so weak from hunger that I could not, even if I wanted to, which I don't."

Little by little the Indians overcame their fear and came closer, muttering to each other all the while and pointing to the whale. Finally, satisfied that he was indeed helpless, they paddled their canoes right up to his side.

The fishing was good and soon the tribesmen returned with their canoes loaded down with salmon, cod and halibut, which they dumped in the whale's mouth.

"How did you get here?" asked the chief.

The whale shook his head sadly, "I came on the last big tide, over a week ago, and now I cannot get out until the next one."

The Indians looked at one another and said, "Oh," and "Ah," and nodded their heads in sympathy, for they too knew hardship and sorrow. Didn't the forest fires destroy their village and most of their boats only last summer? And didn't they almost starve because of the shortage of game after the summer's fires? In fact, didn't they suffer every year because of the blazing forests? Yes, indeed, they knew sorrow and hardship!

The chief peered intently at the whale. "Then you haven't eaten since you came here?"

The whale shook his head.

"Mercy!" exclaimed the Indians. "He must be almost starved. Come, let us catch some fish for him."

The fishing was good and soon the tribesmen returned with their canoes loaded down with salmon, cod and halibut, which they dumped in the whale's mouth. He ate in great gulps, for he was on the verge of starvation, and so huge a body requires a lot of food.

When he had finished eating, the Indians again gathered around him in their canoes. "We will bring you food each day," announced the chief, "so that when the big tides come again you will be strong enough to make your way out to sea."

The whale looked at his new friends with tears in his eyes. "You are very good," he said, "you could have killed me as I lay helpless and had meat for many days, as well as bone and oil."

The Indians smiled. "We have lots of meat and the fishing is good just now." Then their faces became grave. "Our only real problem is the forest fires, which keep us always in a state of worry during the summer."

"Perhaps I can help you," said the whale thoughtfully. "Sometimes, when I go into the far north, I see the Great Spirit. I will tell him of your kindness and ask him to help you overcome the forest fires."

The Indians thanked the whale politely, wondering, perhaps, why he did not call on the Great Spirit for help for himself. The whale seemed to read their thoughts. "I would have asked him to help me," he said, "but he is in the far north at this time of the year and I am sure he would never hear my cries. He is my friend, though, and I am sure he will help you."

Weeks later, when the tides were high enough for the whale to pass over the sandbars, he swam away into the open sea, free at last. Just before he sank from sight of his waving friends, he called, "I have not forgotten my promise. I will speak to the Great Spirit."

After the whale left, the weather became hotter and hotter. One particularly hot day, as everything sweltered beneath the burning rays of the midsummer sun, a dread cry rang through the woods. "Fire! F-I-R-E! F-I-R-E! ! !"

Soon huge columns of smoke were rolling up into the red sky, and the roar of the onrushing flames shook the earth. Louder and louder grew the sound, until the shouting voices of the Indians could no longer be heard as they hurried with frantic speed to save what they could. The dense smoke climbed higher and the sun faded from sight, as though to hide its face from the scene of terror below.

It was tragic! Mothers rushed hither and thither in search of their children. The men of the tribe struggled to get a few household belongings and their canoes into the water before the fire struck. Youngsters huddled together in fear. A few deer wandered into the clearing, stared around in a dazed fashion and then dashed back, panic-stricken, into the flames. The feverish activity, useless for the most part—the destruction of game and food—the terror—the heartbreaks—horrible marks of the raging tyrant, forest fire.

The Indians worked desperately, but the fire gained in spite of their efforts. The woods were too dry, and the hot winds kept the flames fanned to a white heat. . . It seemed that nothing could save the forests and the village.

Just as the Indians were about to give up hope and take to their canoes, a strange light came over the forests. The heavy, yellowish, smoky air took on a bluish tinge. The wind became cooler. And wonder of wonders, a drop of rain fell. Another—another and another. Faster and faster came the drops, until it seemed that the heavens had opened up and were pouring their entire supply of moisture down on the fire-tortured earth below.

The delighted Indians dropped on their hands and knees in the gathering pools. They threw the water over their heads with their cupped hands, and drank greedily from the fast-forming puddles in the rocks. The chief held back from the rest. Here, he realized, was indeed a miracle. His thoughts went to their friend the whale, and a smile touched his lips. This must be his doing. He had kept his promise.

The rain continued until not a single smouldering ember remained, and the trees in the forests were dripping clean water from every sprig. The grasses and ferns raised their drooping heads and drank in the life-giving moisture. The whole land seemed renewed, and green and alive.

After the sound of rejoicing died down a little, the chief called his tribe together and spoke to them. "The rains came just in time. A few minutes more and the fire would have burned our homes to the ground and destroyed the surrounding forests. Our friend, the whale, promised he would ask the Great Spirit to help us. Perhaps this is his way."

The Indians nodded and listened. The chief went on. "We will lift our hands to the skies in thanks, and if it starts to rain again we will know the rain was sent by the Great Spirit, and that our friend, the whale, has kept his promise."

Hardly had the people raised their hands to the skies than the rain came pouring down, harder even than before. Puddles formed in every little hollow, and each crease in the earth became a small river. The Indians stood and let the rain beat down on their upraised faces, while they chanted the praises of the Great Spirit and the whale. All day and all night the shouting lasted, until even the hardiest warriors sank down, too tired to move any more.

The chief watched, nodding smiling approval from time to time. It was good to see his people so happy. It was good, too, to know that the Great Spirit had not forgotten them, and it was good to know they had such a friend as the whale. "When the feasting is over," he mused, "we will find some way to honour our friend. Maybe we will put him in our totems. Yes, that would be nice. . ."

So now, hundreds of years later, on those far northern shores, rain falls nearly every day—300 inches a year—and the white men grumble and wish with all their hearts they could be dry; but the Indians look at the teeming rain, the green forests filled with game, and their homes so safe from

Hardly had the people raised their hands to the skies than the rain came pouring down, harder even than before.

fire, and they smile as they carve the whale into their totems, for they know of the terrible fires that swept these tree-clad mountains before the whale spoke to the Great Spirit for them, and they rejoice in the life-saving, life-giving, rain.

The Tongue-licked People

SLOWLY Lutraisuh rocked back and forth, cuddling her baby in her arms and cooing soft, guttural Nass River songs in his ears. From time to time she looked up fearfully, and at each sound of footsteps she quickly made sure that the baby was completely covered by his otter robe, tucking in the corners so that only his small face showed. The young woman had good reason for her fears, for if her husband, Qawaek, a big, wicked Haida brave, found out that her baby was a boy he would quickly put an end to its life, just as he had their first two children, both of whom had been boys. Lutraisuh told her husband the new baby was a girl, and so he let it live. . .

Lutraisuh did not belong to the Haida people. She had been captured during a raid on a Nass River tribe, and kept alive because of her beauty. Later she became the wife of Qawaek. Her brothers, with whom she lived on the Nass, had both been killed during the raid, by her Haida husband, who now feared that if any of his sons were allowed to live they might grow up to avenge the death of their uncles. Qawaek smothered the first two babies, both boys, and would surely have treated the third the same way, had not Lutraisuh made him believe that it was a girl baby.

Driven by fear for the safety of her child, Lutraisuh, together with members of a friendly Raven tribe, plotted to destroy Qawaek when he called to see her that night. So the unfortunate woman sat and rocked, torn between fear for her child and fear of her husband, for she well knew what would happen if they failed.

At last she heard his shuffling step before the hut. She reached out her hand in warning to her allies, the Raven people, who were waiting behind the back wall of the bark hut, made sure again the baby was covered, and drew aside the door flap. Qawaek grunted a greeting and pushed his way inside, and, without a glance at his wife, threw himself down on a pile of robes in one corner.

Lutraisuh looked at him in disgust, steeled herself for what she knew must be done, and then gave the signal to her friends. It was all over in a second. The spears and knives went home without a sound; so quiet and swift was the act that the baby did not awaken.

The young woman gathered together a few of her belongings, snatched up the sleeping baby, and hurried to a canoe which the Raven people had hidden on the beach for her escape to the mainland. She laughed harshly as she climbed into the light craft—she and her baby were free at last—she had waited a long time for this moment.

Perhaps if Lutraisuh had known how hard the trip would be across Hecate Straits, from the Queen Charlotte Islands to the mainland, she would have thought twice before starting out on her rash journey. Three days and three nights she battled the rolling tossing sea. . . Seventy hours without sleep. . . Seventy hours of steady paddling. . . Seventy hours in a stormy sea with a baby to feed and protect.

The waves climbed mountain high to fall away in sudden

sloping valleys and send the canoe crashing down, so that each moment seemed it must surely be the last, but Lutraisuh, half frozen and numb from lack of sleep, kept steadily on.

Just when she felt that she lacked the strength to paddle another foot a head of land loomed through the fog, and favourable currents swept her into the shelter of a small cove. She had barely strength enough left to make the canoe fast before she fell into the complete sleep of utter exhaustion.

How long she slept, Lutraisuh did not know, but she awakened with a start to find the canoe surrounded by strange Indians. She screamed and turned to find her baby. He was gone! She swung around, her eyes wide with fear, "My child," she screamed, "what have you done with him?"

One of the men, who seemed to be the leader, spoke to her in a tongue not unlike her own and which she could readily understand, "The baby is safe. The women are feeding him. And you will be safe too; we only waited for you to awaken to take you to our village. You had a hard voyage and you were very tired. It was better to allow you to finish your sleep."

Lutraisuh's face relaxed. She was among friends. "Thank you," she said simply. "You are kind."

The baby was given the name of Naeqt, or Tongue-licked, because Lutraisuh was supposed to have licked his face to keep the salt sea from blistering his cheeks during the terrible journey across the Straits. He was readily accepted as a member of the tribe, but there was always something different about Naeqt; he was crueler and fiercer than his playmates and he quickly learned that he was stronger than they, and he used his strength to make himself their leader. There was a cunning, too, about the boy that was unusual in one so young. . . He managed to get most of the things he wanted by means of his wits, and without much work.

During this period of his youth Naeqt found himself often before the council of elders to explain his behaviour, or rather, misbehaviour. These sessions, which usually ended with a thrashing for the boy, only seemed to make him more anxious to defy the laws of the tribe and live according to his own will.

After an extra long series of crimes, the tribesmen grew tired of his evil ways and drove both Naeqt and his mother from the village, and warned them never to return on pain of death.

For years they wandered homeless, hunting and fishing for a living, with Naeqt growing wilder and more powerful every day. He learned to use a bow far beyond the strength of an ordinary man, and soon he was able to kill even such fierce animals as grizzly bears, while small game fell easy prey to his skill. This made the problem of getting food fairly simple and gave the young man time to think of other things, chiefly conquest and a wife.

He talked over his desires with his mother and they decided that he should raid a village and carry off a young woman as his bride. In preparation for this foray Lutraisuh made her son a strange coat from the skin of a large grizzly he had killed. She turned the fur side in and covered the outside with small slabs of slate, which made it look and feel like a coat of mail. When the odd coat was finished Naeqt took his bow and drove arrow after arrow against it. The shafts fell to the ground without a single one piercing the slate armour.

In addition to the grizzly bear coat Naeqt fashioned himself a huge club, which his great strength enabled him to twirl around like a match stick. Later this club was named the Strike-but-once club and said to possess magic powers, but probably the magic was the awful strength of Naeqt's right arm.

Armed with his mighty club, his peerless bow, and protected by the slate-covered coat, Naeqt set off confidently on
his first raid. He and his mother had chosen a village and
carefully planned every move. He was to walk into the village at a time when few warriors were around, seize a
maiden and carry her off, trusting to the boldness of the
move to give it success.

Everything went as they planned. Naeqt walked into the
village, wandered from one hut to another, peering at the
maidens to find one that suited his fancy. The people looked
at him with mild surprise and a few even offered him greetings. It was almost too easy. At last he found a plump,
strong-looking squaw standing a little way from the huts.
He swept her up over his shoulder, struck down a bewildered
warrior who made a half-hearted attempt to bar his way,
and trotted off into the woods with his prize.

A little way up the mountain he met his mother and
together they rushed the girl to a hiding-place they had prepared before. The maiden accepted her fate with little fuss.
It was the usual thing among the Indians for young men to
raid villages and carry off women, and Naeqt was not
unpleasant to the maiden's eyes.

The hue and cry lasted for most of that day and part of
the next as the villagers carried out their search for the bold
raider. Naeqt, instead of staying in hiding, spent his time
waylaying warriors who got too far from the main party. His
deeds were discovered late in the second afternoon of the
search. When the number he had killed was totalled the
searchers concluded there must be a large war party out and
returned to their village to make ready to withstand a siege.
Naeqt and his mother laughed together when they saw what

Naturally, too, he was joined by other renegades, until he had a formidable little army at his disposal.

was happening, a whole village hiding itself against the ravages of one man!

After his first success Naeqt undertook more and more daring raids till his fame spread far and wide. He became known as the Grizzly Bear and he boasted that resistance against him was useless. Naturally, too, he was joined by other siwashed or outlawed Indians, until he had a wicked little army at his command. He became a power to reckon with, a power of evil.

There comes a time when a bandit whether big or small, annoys honest people to the point where they make an effort great enough to destroy him, and so it was with Naeqt.

As long as he had only to face single tribes or villages Naeqt could achieve easy victories, but when faced with a union, or federation of tribes, the strength of numbers was against him and his defeat was certain. The wily Naeqt knew this and part of his sly plan was to keep the various tribes in his district fighting amongst themselves so that their strength was always divided. But at last he carried his ravages too far and the Indians of the Lower Nass River and the Kitamat district banded together to destroy him.

Naeqt knew that unless he did something drastic, and fast, his life and his robber band would soon come to a sudden and, to him, untimely end. He decided to build a fortress from which he could strike out hard and fast, and return to shelter before the enemy had time to take action against him. For this purpose he founded Ta'awdzep, about two miles from Kitwanga, on a high point of rock, which could be easily defended. Along the main trail he set up rock traps which could be sprung from within the fortress, and at other points he placed dry cedar planks covered with deer hooves, which would rattle and give the alarm if touched. The fort itself was made of logs ten feet high, and supplied with food and water to stand a siege of several months.

From this stronghold Naeqt continued his robbery and raiding in spite of the united efforts of most of the local tribes to stop him. He seemed to bear a charmed life, and certainly he feared nothing.

His end came in a very odd manner. He was shot to death by the first gun owned by an Indian in the Nass River country.

The Lower Nass River and Kitamat chieftains heard of a strange, new weapon which possessed unusual powers. They finally managed to buy one—a gun, of course—from a Russian trader, who agreed to train one of the Indians in its use.

When it was felt that the brave had become a good enough shot with the new weapon, the warriors of several villages set off to destroy their old enemy. They did not try to hide themselves and the deer hooves set up a terrific din as the braves forced their way past. Naeqt rushed to the door of the fort, pulling on his coat of armour as he ran, to see who dared invade his terrible castle. The gun boomed as Naeqt pounded through the main door of the fort and he fell just beyond the gate, shot through the breast and mortally wounded. In half an hour he was dead.

Lutraisuh and Naeqt's wife were both put to death, together with those members of the band who had not escaped. The fort was burned to the ground, and Naeqt's coat of mail and weapons were burned at a huge pow-wow to celebrate his death.

The tales of the ravages of this vicious bandit and the adventures of his mother are told on totem poles both on the Queen Charlotte Islands and the mainland, and the people who own the Tongue-licked crest still boast with pride of Naeqt, their first ancestor.

Naeqt fell, shot through the breast and mortally wounded.

The Legend of the Thunderbird

AMONG the totem-pole-carving Indians of the British Columbia and Alaska coast the Thunderbird is the outstanding figure. The frog, the whale, the real kingfisher, and the two-headed snake each belong to individual tribes, but the Thunderbird, and only the Thunderbird, seems to be common property, and is by far the most widely used and highly respected of all the figures carved on the totem poles.

There might be no carving of the Thunderbird had it not been for a small Indian boy with a twisted foot, for it was he who first saw the big bird and whittled its likeness.

The little boy was called Twisted Foot because of his injured foot, for, like most Indians, he took his name from his most noticeable feature. He could not run and play like the rest of the children, so he spent his time watching the tribal carvers at work on the totem poles, and dreaming of the day when he, too, would be a great carver. Often he asked to help, but the men only laughed and said he would have to grow up first, or else they told him he would have to carve a picture of the thunder that rolled across their skies so often before he could be accepted as a carver.

As time went on, and Twisted Foot continued to watch the carvers—for while they did not allow him to help, neither did they drive him away—he became expert in picking out the flaws in the cedar logs selected for carving, and often his plans regarding the placing of certain figures were accepted.

Once, when Twisted Foot was thirteen, he pleaded harder than ever with the carvers to let him help, but as always before, they only laughed and promised he should help when he could carve them a picture of the rolling thunder. Downhearted, the boy limped slowly and sadly to the beach, where he sat and gazed at the oily sea through tear-filled eyes. While he was sitting thus a loud clap of thunder boomed across the water and, strangely enough, it seemed to come from just around a nearby point. Twisted Foot sat up. If he could only see the thunder, or what made it, then perhaps he could carve a totem of it. He quickly made up his mind. He would seek the thunder, even if it took the rest of his life.

Ten minutes later the Indian boy was paddling his canoe towards the point, from beyond which the thunder seemed to come. Just as he rounded the tongue of land, another roar pounded the air; this time from beyond the next corner. Twisted Foot paddled for that point, only to discover when he got there the sound came from some place still farther ahead. So it was for the rest of that day, and the next, and the next, and for many days to come. Always the thunder seemed just around the next point.

Twisted Foot kept on with his search, stopping only long enough to sleep and pick a few berries for food. He had his heart set on seeing what made the thunder and winning for himself a place among the carvers.

One morning as Twisted Foot sat in his canoe, wondering if it would not be wise to give up his search until spring and return to his tribe for the winter, the sea suddenly began to boil. His canoe pitched from side to side, and, expert as he

He spent his time watching the carvers at work and dreaming of the day when he, too, would be a great carver.

was with a paddle, he had trouble keeping the light craft from turning over. The sea tossed violently and a broad back came to the surface with a mighty boiling of water. It was the largest whale the boy had ever seen. It turned its head in every direction, and rolled its eyes fearfully for a minute, then started swimming as fast as it could for the open sea.

Twisted Foot watched and wondered as he steadied his canoe, for it was most unusual to see a whale making off in haste, as almost all the creatures in the sea live in mortal fear of these monsters, which, in turn, fear hardly anything. But this whale was fleeing in terror.

Just as these thoughts raced through the little Indian's mind, a huge, swift-moving shadow darkened the sky. He quickly turned his face upwards. There, diving down on the terrified whale, was the largest bird he had ever seen, far larger even than the whale.

Like a shot the big bird dropped on the fleeing monster. It seized the whale by the back and without effort carried it squirming into the sky. Higher and higher the bird rose with its burden until finally, when almost out of sight, it released its hold and allowed the whale to come streaking down towards the water. It hit with a big splash, and the waves it made crashed on the nearby shore causing a booming, rumbling roar—THUNDER!

Little Twisted Foot could hardly believe his eyes and ears. He became so excited he stood up in his canoe and shouted... He had found the thunder! He had seen the big bird making it! For a moment he forgot all else. The huge shadow again passing over his head brought him rudely back to earth. He looked up to find the bird hanging in the sky just overhead.

"Who are you?" the bird asked.

"I am known as Twisted Foot," replied the boy, "and some day I hope to be a great carver."

"Aren't you afraid of me?"

"No, I'm not." Twisted Foot answered truthfully, for he felt no fear of the big bird, strangely enough.

"Hrrrrrrrumph!" snorted the bird, watching the boy and at the same time keeping an eye on the whale, which was trying to escape unnoticed. "What are you doing here?"

"I came to find the thunder."

"Well, well, well!" the bird exclaimed, still watching the whale out of the corner of one eye. "Now that you have found it, what are you going to do?"

"I shall return to my tribe," said the boy, his eyes shining, "and carve huge totem poles with you, the Thunderbird, as their topmost figure. People will know from these poles that the Thunderbird is the mightiest of all the birds."

"Oh, I see," said the bird, preening his feathers, for he was very vain. "On the very top, eh? Well, that WOULD be nice. I'll take you home so you can start carving right away."

The bird's strong wings quickly carried Twisted Foot back to his village, and while the whole tribe watched open-mouthed, the Thunderbird set the boy down on the beach before his father's hut.

As the bird flew away he called back over his shoulder, "Don't forget your promise. Put me on the very top of the poles."

Twisted Foot, of course, was at once accepted as a carver, and soon his first pole, with the Thunderbird, wings outstretched, perched on the very top, looked out over the open sea.

During his life the crippled Indian carved many poles, each with the Thunderbird as the topmost figure. In later

Like a shot the big bird dropped on the fleeing monster.

years he allowed other tribes to adopt the figure, provided they always carved it in the highest position.

From time to time, so the story goes, the Thunderbird used to come and visit with his friend Twisted Foot, and pose for him in order that the figures he carved might be exactly like him, and also to make sure, so it is said, that he was always placed at the very top of the poles.

The Story of the Grateful Wolf

LONG, long, ago a branch of the Wild Rice clan moved from their old home in the Wild Rice village to a new hunting-ground on the upper Skeena, near the present Indian town of Gitwinlkul and they named their new home Ksen-dehl-tsan, or River of Mists. They took unto themselves, as a special mark, the crest of the running wolves, which was later shown on their totem poles by a wolf facing towards the top.

Shortly after they were settled in their new home they awakened one morning to find a large wolf sitting near the door of the big, log lodge, or wilp-qan, in which the whole family-clan lived. The household chief, Ramlu-geedels, questioned the visitor, whom they made welcome since he was a wolf. "What are you doing here, brother?"

The wolf did not answer, but instead sat and stared with tears in his eyes.

"Perhaps he is hungry," suggested one of the squaws.

"Perhaps," agreed the chief. "Bring him some venison."

The wolf, however, refused all food and continued to sit and stare sadly at the tribesmen. From time to time he would stretch his neck and cough. The Indians were puzzled and walked around the dog-like beast, talking to one another in

Finally they looked in the wolf's throat, and there, sure enough, was a firmly lodged fish bone.

their gutteral tones. A wolf who would not eat was a curiosity indeed.

"He seems ill," said Ramlu-geedels. "You, nephews, examine him and see if there is anything wrong. Maybe he is hurt."

The young men, Weeraihs and Ligiralwil, went up to the wolf gingerly and began their examination. The wolf, as soon as he saw what they were doing, opened his mouth wide, as though trying to draw attention to his throat. Finally they looked in his throat and there sure enough, was a firmly lodged fish bone. It took but a second for the young men to work it free.

When the bone was gone the wolf shook his head hard, then went to the food and ate heartily. His stomach filled, he stood before the chief, Ramlu-geedels, and spoke for the first time. "You and your people have saved my life. I will help you if ever I can. Now may I stay in your lodge until I am strong enough to take the trail again?"

The wolf was soon as good as ever, and the Indians awoke one morning to find their strange friend gone.

Months passed and winter came again. The summer had not been good; fishing had been poorer than usual, and the hunting had been so bad in the fall that it hardly paid the men to go out. As the winter went on the food supply shrank rapidly, for they were not able to add to it as they usually could by hunting, or fishing through the ice. True, they hunted and fished every day, but only once in a while did they get anything. The men grew lean, the women wore a tired, worried look, and the children got thinner and thinner, until their bodies were just bundles of bones under tightly stretched skin. The smaller children, the babies, cried most of the time, unable to understand the hunger that gnawed at their tiny stomachs.

February, always the hunger month in the north, found the Indians at the end of their supplies. The food was all gone. They were too weak to hunt. Even the fire in the middle of the lodge was allowed to get smaller and smaller, so they had to huddle around it in a shivering little group, trying to keep warm. No one spoke, for there was nothing to say. The spirit of death was about to lay its cold hands on them, and they all knew it.

Ramlu-geedels sat a little apart from the rest, as befitted a chieftain, even in the face of death. Here, he thought bitterly, ended his mighty plans for the new clan. How much better to have stayed with the main tribe; at least there would have been enough to eat. He felt to blame for the disaster that was about to overtake them. He pounded his knee with his fist; if there was only something he could do!

A cry from the darkness outside broke in on his unpleasant thoughts.

"Hiya!" cried the voice. "You, Wolf People, inside the lodge!"

Ramlu-geedels' eyes lit up. He gathered his strength and dragged himself to the entrance. Perhaps the visitors brought food. Peering through the hole above the door the chief could only make out a dark blur against the snow. For a second he was afraid, then thinking of the sad plight of his people, he flung wide the door. Leading from the steps were prints, prints which he knew at once to be those of their friend the wolf.

"Wolf People, follow me and I will lead you to food," the big wolf cried.

The Indians looked at one another questioningly. This

In the middle of the clearing lay five shapes, which the men
knew, even before they got close, were the bodies of caribou.

might be a trick to get them outside and kill them. Perhaps the wolves were starving too. Then they shrugged. What did it matter? Unless they got food they could only live a short time at best. . .

The chief and Weeraihs, one of his nephews, put on their warmest clothes and followed the wolf. They were very weak and many times during the short journey the wolf had to sit and wait for them. They noticed that his belly was rounded out even though his ribs showed, meaning that he had eaten well lately, but had been nearly starving before.

The wolf led the men through the waist-deep snow for a distance of about a mile, then he turned off the main trail. In the middle of a clearing lay five shapes, which Ramlu-geedels and Weeraihs knew, even before they got close, were the bodies of caribou. The men fell on the animals like wild beasts, tore off chunks of the frozen meat and gnawed it down greedily.

The wolf watched the half-starved men eat. He wore a satisfied look on his face, as though pleased at his friends' enjoyment. At last, when he thought they had eaten all they could, he spoke to them in their own tongue. "It is good that we found the caribou, or all of us should have starved. They came in sight yesterday and we killed most of them. This meat will last you, with care, until the fish come again into the rivers."

The men tried to thank their strange benefactor, but he would not wait and ran off into the woods with a backward shout, "We are brothers and must help each other."

The two men hacked off a large chunk of meat which Ramlu-geedels carried back to the lodge on his shoulders, while Weeraihs remained to stand guard over the rest.

The scene at the lodge was wonderful to watch, and

Ramlu-geedels' heart gladdened as his people fell on the raw meat. When they had eaten their fill, he told them they owed their lives to the wolf and they added their thanks to his.

The meat saved the clan and the following winter found them prepared for the famine months. Ramlu-geedels realized his dream, for the family grew great and strong. The wolf never returned to visit the lodge, but the tribe carved a totem pole in his honour, which they erected at Gitwinlkul many years later as a monument to Ligi-ralwil, one of Ramlu-geedels' nephews.

Kaigyet, the Strong Man or
The Cross-Eyed Indian People

GYAEDEM-SKANEES, which means mighty hunter, and his pretty squaw, Neegy, were in the habit of hunting farther afield than the rest of the tribesmen, and their catches were larger and better than those of the more timid, who stayed close to the main village. It was on one of these distant trips that this venturesome pair had their most trying adventure and started a chain of happenings which led to a whole tribe being cross-eyed.

Many miles from the main village they chose a camp by the side of a lake and Gyaedem, as we shall call him from now on, left his wife to finish making camp while he went in search of small game for the pot. Hunting was poor and he was gone for some hours. When he returned he was surprised to find the camp deserted and no sign of Neegy.

For a little while he sat by the still smouldering fire, thinking she might have gone in search of some special bark or roots, or perhaps was trying to catch some fish for their evening meal. As it grew darker, with no sign of Neegy, Gyaedem became worried and finally decided to scout the edge of the camp for tracks. Hardly had he left the light cast by the campfire when he stopped short in open-mouthed amazement. There at his feet, clearly outlined even in the dusk were the largest footprints he had ever seen, fully five times as large as his own, which were large enough. A little more careful searching led him to believe that the huge man, whoever he might be, had kidnapped Neegy!

Gyaedem was furious. After all, it is one thing to steal ordinary women from a village and quite another to take the wife of the mightiest hunter in the district! He clinched his teeth until his jaw muscles bunched in a hard knot! His eyes gleamed with rage! He snatched up his bow and quiver of arrows and started at a fast trot on the track of the villain.

The trail led around the lake, with the giant making no attempt to hide. Gyaedem, nose pointed to the ground, followed at a dead run, hoping to arrive before the monster had time to harm his good wife, Neegy.

Just as the dawn was breaking, Gyaedem caught his first glimpse of the kidnapper. The sight made him gasp. The giant stood on the shore of the lake looking back, as though he intended to allow himself to be overtaken. In spite of his anger, Gyaedem felt awed and slacked his speed, for never before had he seen such a huge, threatening figure of a man. He stood twenty feet tall, with great wide shoulders. His legs looked like good-sized fir logs, with the moss still on them. He was naked, except for the shaggy hide of some animal, which he wore around his middle like a kilt. His dirty, straggly hair was unkempt and hung in matted strands about his face. Gyaedem quieted his trembling hands and reached for his bow.

Just as he was about to release his first arrow, the giant reached behind his back and with an evil grin held up Neegy. For a second Gyaedem held back, then, with a prayer to the Great Spirit, he let the arrow fly. It struck the giant fairly on the chest, bringing out a few drops of blood before it

Gyaedem gasped, for on the palm of the giant's hand was the figure of a heart!

dropped, broken, to the beach. Quickly Gyaedem fitted another arrow on the string and let it fly. The result was the
same. The giant, in the meantime, stood grinning down at
the angry young man.

"Ah ha," he exclaimed, "your arrows are too dull . . . or
your arm too weak," he added with a sneer.

Gyaedem gritted his teeth and loosed another shaft. It,
too, fell to the ground without doing any damage.

"Now, my little sparrow," said the giant, still grinning
evilly, "it is my turn."

He reached out his free hand to seize the hunter. Gyaedem
gasped, for on the palm of the giant's hand was the figure of
a heart. He thought fast. Perhaps the monster's heart was in
his hand, and not in his body at all. It was a desperate chance,
but he was desperate. He sped an arrow into the heart-shaped
pattern. The giant stopped dead in the middle of his half-
completed reaching motion, a stunned look of pain twisted
the grin on his face, and he toppled to the sand without a
sound. Gyaedem waited a minute with drawn bow ready for
another shot, but his foe did not move. At last he stepped
forward, took a firm grip on his enemy's eye lashes, and pulled
one big eye open; the eyeball was rolled back, the eye was
sightless. The giant was dead!

Neegy ran to her husband and threw her arms about his
neck. She wept in body-shaking sobs. He patted her head and
tried to comfort her, asking her to dry her tears and rejoice
with him on their lucky escape.

When her sobs finally stopped, she raised her face to her
husband. "Yes," she said, her voice still hoarse, "the giant is
dead, but our danger is not past. His son lives on!"

"But where is the son?" asked Gyaedem, looking around.

"Under his father's hair," whispered Neegy.

The young hunter lifted up the giant's hair, and there, huddled out of sight, was an exact copy of the monster man, except on a much smaller scale, of course.

The youngster and Gyaedem eyed each other for a minute, as though each were taking the other's measure.

"What is your name?" Gyaedem asked. "That is, if you have one."

The boy scowled, "Oh, I have one, all right. It's Kaigyet, and you'd better kill me now, because I'm going to kill you when I grow up, if I live that long."

The hunter laughed. The idea of a boy like this killing him was too funny for words. After all, he had been mighty enough to kill the father, so there should be little to fear from the half-grown son. "Come," he said, "let us be friends. I killed your father in a fair fight. You are a good-looking young brave, my wife and I will adopt you, if you are willing."

The giant-boy wrinkled his brow in thought, looking from one to the other of his companions through half-shut eyes, as though trying to read in the faces whether they could be trusted. At last he nodded assent.

Neegy clung to Gyaedem. "Be wary, my husband, this boy is evil, just as his father, but without the vulnerable spot on his palm. . . Given a chance he will surely kill us."

Gyaedem laughed, "Nonsense, my dear, this is only a boy. He will grow to be as fond of us as he was of his father. Wait and see."

Years passed and Kaigyet throve on the good and plentiful food he got at the village. He grew rapidly and by the time he had reached his eighteenth summer he was taller and heavier than his father had been, and he gave promise of growing still more. But as he grew taller, his temper grew shorter. He sat on his haunches before Gyaedem's hut and growled at everyone who tried to come near. He hated everybody, particularly his foster-father.

One night, while the camp slept, Kaigyet rose from his couch of furs and slunk silently from hut to hut, killing the sleepers. He managed to slay all the tribesmen in camp. Then, grinning with mad delight, he collected the eyes and tongues of his victims so they could not see his future evil deeds or tell the Great Spirit on him. He put all the eyes and tongues in a big basket near his hut.

In his haste to kill the tribesmen, Kaigyet overlooked the three virgins, who were away saying their prayers to the Great Spirit. Now, to the coastal Indians, or certain tribes of them, the tribal virgins are important personages. They serve very much the same purpose as the witch doctors or shamans and know all about roots and herbs, both good and bad. In Kaigyet's tribe they were also famous for their cooking.

The three virgins arrived back in camp just in time to find the monster, Kaigyet, preparing a feast. They saw at a glance what had taken place, and realizing that they could not escape as they had already been seen, walked up to the giant as though nothing unusual had happened.

"Greetings, Kaigyet," called the oldest and wisest virgin, "I see you are about to feast."

Kaigyet grunted and nodded his head.

"Perhaps we can help you," she continued. "You know we are the best cooks in the tribe."

The giant's eyes lit up and he nodded vigorously, pointing to the stewing-pot to show that he was delighted to turn the job over to them.

The virgins rolled back the sleeves of their cedar bark gowns and began adding roots and herbs to the contents of the pot. In a few minutes the most savoury steam imaginable curled up from the stew. Kaigyet, who had been watching what they were doing with a greedy eye, leaned far over to breathe in the smell of the stew, grunting with delight.

The sisters continued to stir and urged the monster to whiff again and again. He was more than willing and was soon leaning right over the pot, breathing deeply. Gradually his eyelids began to get heavy, and he felt a great desire to sleep. In fact, it was only with a mighty effort that he managed to stay awake.

"Why don't you lie down for a while, Kaigyet?" one of the virgins purred. "We will call you when the meal is ready."

Kaigyet stared stupidly at each of the women in turn, hardly able to keep his eyes open.

"Yes," he mumbled, "that's it, I need sleep. You'll call me when the stew is cooked enough—" His voice trailed off, his head fell forward and he sank into a deep sleep.

Almost as soon as his eyes were tightly closed the virgins snatched up knives and fell upon the helpless monster. Again and again they stabbed him, until there was no possible chance of any life remaining. Once they were sure Kaigyet was dead, they rushed to the basket and turned its contents on the ground. The assortment of eyes and tongues rolled on the grass.

One by one they dragged the dead Indians over to the fire and fitted each of them with a tongue and two eyes. Then they said a few magic words over the body and presto, it came to life again.

The three women worked very hard and soon all the tribesmen were back on their feet, dancing around the virgins and hailing them as the saviours of the tribe, which indeed they were.

It was the alert Gyaedem, Kaigyet's foster-father, who first discovered the mistake.

It was the ever-alert Gyaedem, Kaigyet's foster-father, who first discovered the mistake.

"Look!" he cried, "Whale Hunter, the chief, has one brown eye and one black! And his daughter is cross-eyed! My wife, Neegy, who used to talk all the time, has not said a dozen words in the last hour, while Young Eagle, who is noted for his silence, has chattered steadily in a woman's voice ever since his life was given back."

"Wah!" grunted the chief, turning his daughter round and peering at her eyes, "it is true. The eyes and tongues have been mixed. The virgins have not given us our own back."

For a while there was great anger among the tribesmen, for no one likes to have one big eye and one small one, and no woman likes to speak with a deep bass voice, while her husband, a mighty hunter, squeaks like a coy maiden. However, order was restored at last and the people remembered that the virgins had given their lives back, and admitted that it was better to be mixed up than dead. They continued to honour the virgins.

An Indian named Samalee carved the story on a totem pole near Hagwelget, and even to this day there are some mighty strange voices in the district, and more cross-eyed people than in any other part of the neighbouring country.

The Mystery of the Forbidden Plateau

L ONG before the advent of the white man, the Comox Indians, a branch of the Cowichan Tribe, lived around where the town of Courtenay, on Vancouver Island, now stands. They fished, hunted and generally led a quiet, uneventful life. They were a peaceful tribe, and as most of their living came easily, they were lazier and weaker than most of the coast Indians. It is said they preferred fishing to hunting because it required less work. . . To add to their comforts, they lived on the inside, or eastern slope of Vancouver Island and so were sheltered from the more serious storms that so often pounded the other side of the island. Everything came to them with little effort and, as a result, they grew softer and softer, year by year.

The Alberni Indians were Nootkans and lived in almost the opposite manner to the Comox, even though their homes were hardly fifty miles apart. They were hardly, war-like men, who would rather take something from an enemy by force than earn it in a lawful way, even though it might be easier. They built strong canoes and sailed them in the stormiest seas, for the thrill and adventure.

One day an Alberni scout—they were given to making long trips alone—returned to tell of the soft, peaceful tribe

who lived on the other side of the island. He told of their
wealth, and of the ease with which they could be robbed. A
few days later a war party of Albernis swept down on the un-
suspecting Comox Indians. They looted their winter supplies,
killed all the men they could catch, stole the younger women
and set a torch to what they did not want or could not carry.

The few Comoxes who escaped returned to find their
village in ashes, their wives and daughters gone, their best
warriors slain. . . For a few days they mourned their losses,
then hunger and cold forced them to go back to their hunting
and fishing and building.

Months passed and the tribe, all that was left of it,
managed to rebuild the village and refill the store houses
against the coming winter. But they were not to be allowed
to remain in peace. The Albernis struck again and once more
swept the village clean.

This time the work of rebuilding was harder. There were
fewer men to help, and the winter had already set in to add
to their troubles. Hunger, too, became a gnawing problem,
and some of the men had to keep hunting, day after day,
while the women spent every spare moment fishing to add to
the dwindling food supply, or tanning the hides the men
brought in to make badly needed clothes and shelters. For
the first time in the memory of the tribe, the Comoxes knew
cold and hunger.

All this hardship had two effects on the tribesmen. It
hardened their flabby muscles, gone soft through long idle-
ness, and it sharpened their wits to the point where they
were able to defend themselves. Their leaders, too, bright-
ened up and set themselves to find some way of beating the
Albernis, whom they felt sure would strike again.

Many had plans for defending the village, but all of them

were faulty in some way or other. They were too few in numbers to make a stand-up fight of it; besides, they had to think of the women, who would be the chief sufferers if they were defeated. No, they must use their wits, not strength.

Outstanding among the remaining warriors was a young man named Little Bear, and it was he who finally worked out the accepted plan for the expected battle. His scheme was simple enough. They would build pitfalls and rock traps along the trail, and fall upon their enemies during the mix-up that was sure to follow the springing of the traps. The women and children, meanwhile, would be safe in the deep fastness of the Plateau—a mountainous region high above the village.

Little Bear seemed to be untiring during the days before the fight. He helped with the building of the traps, and tested them to be sure they would fall as soon as certain key sticks were removed. He checked each man on the part he was to play. He made the lookout recite his orders a dozen times, and during the last nights before the expected raid he helped the women, children and old men get started on their way to hiding-places in the Plateau. He would stand by the side of the trail patting one on the back, shaming another, and helping another up with her load. He was a tower of strength, and from him the whole tribe drew courage. Men, much older than he, spoke of him in whispers as a great warrior, and a man who would do great deeds and lead the tribe to many victories. . .

Hardly had the non-fighting members of the tribe climbed up the rocky trail than the signal fires of the lookout sent up their warning columns of smoke. A few minutes later, the lookout himself panted into camp to tell his message again. The Albernis were coming!

The warriors looked at one another and for a split second

He was a tower of strength and from him the whole tribe drew
courage and confidence.

panic was very near. It is hard to face an enemy who has beaten you again and again and not feel panic. Little Bear, natural leader that he was, sensed the cold breath of fear that touched his men, and quickly he stepped forward. "Come," he ordered, "get to your stations! Remember our plan." He sounded sure of himself and his bravery quickly spread to the others. The danger was past, and the men went to their posts determined to destroy, once and for all, this danger to their freedom and happiness.

The Albernis, sure of themselves, made the mistake of thinking the Comoxes would still be weak, and marched boldly into the pass. So certain were they of victory that they did not bother to place the usual advance guard.

The Comoxes waited, every eye on Little Bear. The Albernis continued their noisy advance.

When the middle of the raiding column passed beneath the rock trap, Little Bear dropped his hand. The waiting axemen leapt forward. A few swift blows and the whole mass of stone rolled, with a noise like thunder, onto the heads of the amazed Albernis below. As soon as the dust settled enough to see, the Comoxes, quick to press their advantage, swept down on their stunned foes. The few who escaped the rock slide met a hasty end at the hands of the excited, shouting, Comox warriors.

When the fighting ended, the victorious braves returned to say words of thanks to their leader, Little Bear. All the rest of the night they danced and sang his praises. . . They made him chieftain of the tribe, and boasted of great things he would do in the future. The older men sat at the edge of the dancing circle and told each other of victories that would be won, of slaves that would be taken and glorious days to come.

In the morning, Little Bear sent one of the scouts to bring back the women, children and old men.

And here I wish I could end this story, but it is history and there is more to tell. . .

Several hours later the scout returned. His face was covered with dirt and sweat. He staggered past the lines of silent men to where Little Bear stood and sank at his chieftain's feet.

"The women and children," he gasped, "they're gone. I searched everywhere. There's not a trace."

Little Bear snatched the scout to his feet. "Gone?" he shouted. "Are you mad? Where could they go?"

He allowed the nearly worn-out man to slip back to the ground, he needed no other proof than that written on his scout's face. . . What he said was only too true.

Little Bear turned to his men. "Gather 'round me, warriors," he ordered. "Our women are gone. While we fought here some other foe has captured them. Come, we will bring them back and punish their captors."

But they did not bring them back. They searched the Plateau from the highest peak to the deepest valley and not so much as a trace could they find to show what had happened. Little Bear searched alone long after the other men were too tired to go on. Finally, though, even he was forced to admit that the task was hopeless. You could not fight what you could not see.

After they had rested, Little Bear again called the grief-stricken men together. "My people," he began, "our search is hopeless. Our women and children are gone, taken by the evil spirits which dwell in the Plateau. We cannot bring back those already lost, but we can prevent the loss of any more people in this evil place. From this day on it is forbidden to

The Comoxes waited tensely, every eye on Little Bear. The Albernis continued their noisy advance.

all Indians, and it shall be known as the Forbidden Plateau."

The Comox Indians, hardy and war-like as a result of their hardships, stole some women from a weaker tribe and so re-established their village. Little Bear fulfilled the promise of his youth and became a great warrior. Forbidden Plateau remained forbidden and so it is to the Indians even to this day.

The Mountain Goat of Gurhsan

GURHSAN stood before his hut at Gitsegyukla village with his eyes downcast and his brow wrinkled in deep, unpleasant thought. He was the head of a small family-tribe and it was his job to keep law and order. The young man sighed; if the clan would not obey the old laws there was nothing much he could do about it, for all tribal laws were kept only if most of the people wanted them kept. He wondered what would be the wisest course to take, and at last decided to call his men together and make one last attempt to talk them into living good lives again.

When they had gathered Gurhsan stood up and started his speech. "My people," he began, "we have strayed far from the right way of life. You all know that when the maiden Skawah, our ancestress, was taken into the sky as the bride of Rays-of-the-Sun she sent back her children to teach us the best laws of living, and we promised to obey them. One of the first laws commanded us to respect the wild animals, and to kill only what we needed for meat, and to kill them quickly so they suffered little pain.

"Yesterday the hunters went to Rocker Deboule, where the mountain goats live, and killed needlessly half the herds. And that is not all; one young goat was captured and brought to camp, where it suffered torture and shame. This cruel act will surely bring punishment from the Gods of the Sky, who once protected us."

Angry shouts broke out among the warriors. . .

"Gurhsan is an old woman!"

"To follow him is to become a farmer!"

"If you like not our hunting, Gurhsan, stay at home with the squaws."

Gurhsan's eyes shot fire. "Silence, you vermin! Dare you thus address Gurhsan? Would any loud-mouth care to make such shouts with his war club in his hand?"

A deep, uneasy silence followed this outbreak, and several warriors who had been in the front row during the shouting tried to shuffle as quietly as possible to the rear ranks. Gurhsan looked scornfully at them and continued to shame them.

"Well," he shouted finally, "what is it to be? Do you follow me, your chieftain, and obey the laws of Heaven, or do you follow your own greedy wills down the road to disaster?"

The warriors looked at the ground and away from their angry leader's eyes and soon slunk off. Two elders came and stood before Gurhsan after the rest had gone. "It is useless, proud chief. Times have changed, and the power of the Sky is no more. The young warriors see things in a different light than their fathers did. It is better that you go with the tide than attempt to breast it."

Gurhsan looked at the old men with pity. "Your advice is as feeble as your minds and your backbones. You are old and you sound like it. As for me, I shall continue to live according to the laws Skawah sent from the skies with her children, whether I have to breast the tide or not."

He noticed the young goat tied nearby and, snatching up the lead line that held it prisoner, he turned angrily away from his would-be advisors.

Gurhsan lived almost alone during the next few weeks. The young men avoided him for fear of getting their skulls cracked, and the older men stayed away because of his remarks about their courage.   His sole companion was the young goat which he had rescued, and of which he had become very fond. He found the animal to be smart and when he talked to it, for lack of a better companion, it listened quietly and seemed to understand every word he said. At times the goat's listening manner made the young Indian laugh and he would clasp his arms around its neck and muss its coat playfully. They grew to be better friends every day.

Early one morning one of the elders called at Gurhsan's hut. "Greetings, chieftain."

Gurhsan nodded coldly.

"A message has come to us," went on the old man. "It is an invitation and it comes from a new tribe who plan to live on the Stekyawden. They are giving a feast to offer us friendship. We come to ask you, as head of the clan, to go with us."

Gurhsan was on the point of refusing angrily when he happened to glance at the young goat. It was nodding its head rapidly. "Well," he thought, "what harm can come of my going?" He turned again to the elder. "I will go."

The new tribe who had come to live in the mountain goat country and who, strangely enough, called themselves the Mountain Goats, received Gurhsan's people royally. The feast boards were set with every known type of food: deer, bear, goat, a dozen kinds of fish and numerous other foods which had never before been seen on the Skeena.

The feasting lasted far into the night, as Gurhsan joined his tribesmen in a meal for the first time in many weeks.

When the feast was at last over and the clansmen rose to take their leave, Gurhsan was surprised to find the young

As Gurhsan and the goat were picking their way along the trail
a scream rent the air from some distance to the right.

goat at his side, and more surprised when it spoke to him in his own language, "I will lead you home, my friend."

As Gurhsan and the goat were picking their way along the pitch-black trail a scream rent the air from some distance to the right. They stopped and listened. Almost at once another scream of terror and pain came to their ears.

"What was that?" asked Gurhsan.

The young goat looked at his friend, "You are a good man, Gurhsan, and a wise chieftain; but your people are not worthy of you. They have forgotten the laws of the Sky and must now pay for their folly."

Gurhsan threw back his head, "They are still my people. Come, we must save them."

The goat shook his head. "It is no use, mighty chief, they are doomed. By the time we reached them they would all be dead. I have saved you because of your kindness and wisdom, but I could not protect you from my angry relatives, if you tried to interfere now."

Gurhsan's eyes opened wide. "Your relatives? . . . Then the tribe with whom we feasted were really the mountain goats in human form? And this is their revenge for the needless slaughter?"

"That is right," answered the goat. "Now let me lead you back to your village."

When they reached the outskirts of the camp the young goat stopped and turned to Gurhsan. "I must leave you now, but I will be back and with me will come many good tribesmen, far better than those you lost. They will obey you and the Sky laws. Your clan will become stronger and richer than ever."

A week later fifty strong young braves, headed by one who was taller and finer looking than all the rest, walked into

Gurhsan's hut. The chief looked up startled and reached for his weapons. "Who are you?" he asked sharply, "and what do you want?"

The leader of the visitors smiled, "You do not know me, Gurhsan?"

"I know your voice, but not your face," muttered the chief, rubbing his chin thoughtfully, "and yet I seem to know you well."

The other laughed, "I am the little goat whom you saved, and who in turn saved you."

Gurhsan leapt to his feet and hugged his friend. "I am glad to see you, Little Mountain Goat. But tell me, how do you change from goat to man so easily?"

Little Mountain Goat—for so he was named—shook his head and said, "This is the last time I will ever be able to change. We, my companions here and myself, were sent by Rays-of-the-Sun, God of the Skies, to punish your people. We have finished our task and now come to offer our services to you, and join your tribe if you will have us."

"Have you?" shouted the happy Gurhsan. "I can think of nothing I would sooner have. Come, let us order a feast as big as the one you gave on Stekyawden. You shall be my right-hand man. Together we will build such a clan that the whole river will know of our goodness and strength. We will carve many poles to leave the memory of our beginning for the world to read. May our sons, in turn, carve many poles in our honour."

Gurhsan's prophecy came true, for while the tribe remained small it was known far and wide for its goodness and wisdom, as well as its divine origin.

Travellers, both Indian and white, pause on their way through the village to admire the fine totem poles and pay their respects to Gurhsan and the mountain goats.

Travellers, both Indian and white, pause on their way through the village to admire the fine totem poles.